BRAIN ACADEMY
MATHS

MISSION FILE 1

Charlotte Haggis,
Louise Moore and
Richard Cooper

Consultants for NACE:
Elaine Sellars and
Sue Lowndes

nace

RISING STARS

Rising Stars are grateful to the following people for their support in developing this series: Sue Mordecai, Julie Fitzpatrick, Johanna Raffan and Belle Wallace.

NACE, PO Box 242, Arnolds Way, Oxford, OX2 9FR
www.nace.co.uk

Rising Stars Ltd, 22 Grafton Street, London, W1S 4EX
www.risingstars-uk.com

Every effort has been made to trace copyright holders and obtain their permission for the use of copyright materials. The authors and publisher will gladly receive information enabling them to rectify any error or omission in subsequent editions.

All facts are correct at time of going to press.

Published 2004
Reprinted 2005, 2006, 2008, 2010
Text, design and layout © Rising Stars UK Ltd.
TASC: Thinking Actively in a Social Context © Belle Wallace 2004

Editorial: Charlotte Haggis, Louise Moore and Richard Cooper
Editorial Consultants: Elaine Sellars, Sue Lowndes and Sally Harbour
Design: Burville-Riley
Illustrations: Cover and insides – Sue Lee / Characters – Bill Greenhead
Cover design: Burville-Riley

British Library Cataloguing in Publication Data.
A CIP record for this book is available from the British Library.

ISBN: 978-1-904591-35-1

Printed by Craft Print International Limited, Singapore

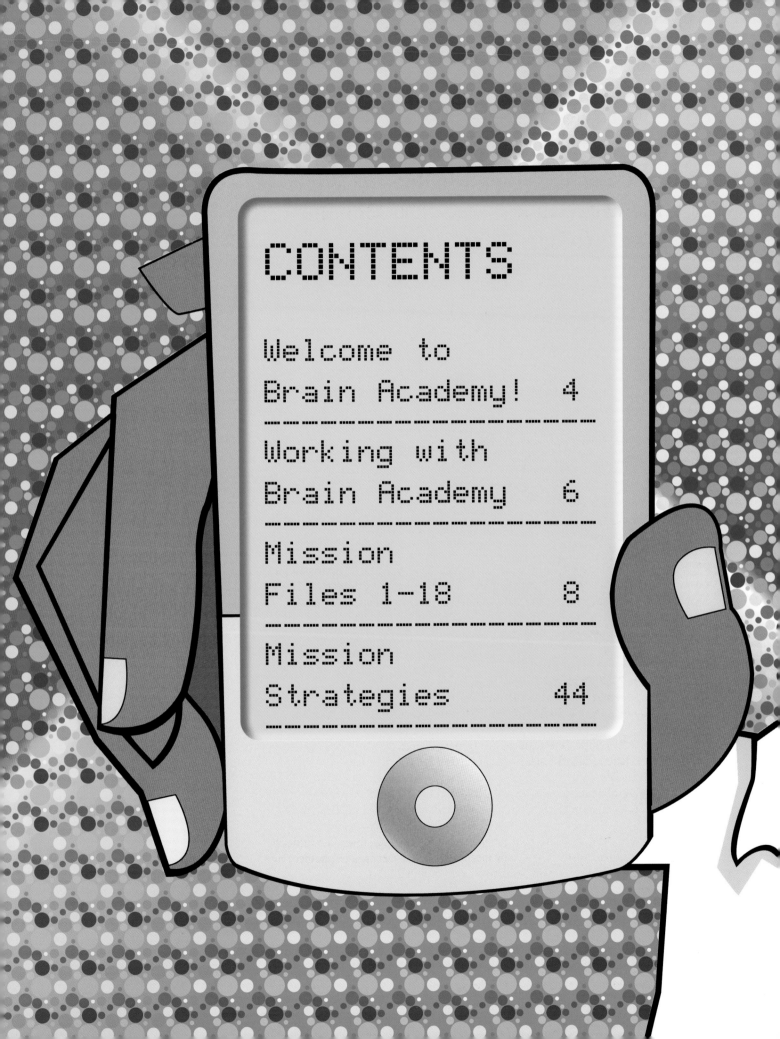

CONTENTS

Welcome to Brain Academy!

Welcome to Brain Academy! Make yourself at home. We are here to give you the low-down on the organisation – so pay attention!

It's our job to help Da Vinci and his colleagues to solve the tough problems they face and we would like you to join us as members of the Academy. Are you up to the challenge?

Da Vinci
Da Vinci is the founder and head of the Brain Academy. He is all seeing, all thinking and all knowing – possibly the cleverest person alive. Nobody has ever actually seen him in the flesh as he communicates only via computer. When Da Vinci receives an emergency call for help, the members of Brain Academy jump into action (and that means you!).

Huxley
Huxley is Da Vinci's right-hand man. Not as clever, but still very smart. He is here to guide you through the missions and offer help and advice. The sensible and reliable face of Brain Academy, Huxley is cool under pressure.

Dr Hood
The mad doctor is the arch-enemy of Da Vinci and Brain Academy. He has set up a rival organisation called D.A.F.T. (which stands for Dull And Feeble Thinkers). Dr Hood and his agents will do anything they can to irritate and annoy the good people of this planet. He is a pain we could do without.

Hilary Kumar
Ms Kumar is the Prime Minister of our country. As the national leader she has a hotline through to the Academy but will only call in an extreme emergency. Confident and strong willed, she is a very tough cookie indeed.

General Cods-Wallop
This highly decorated gentleman (with medals, not wallpaper) is in charge of the armed forces. Most of his success has come from the help of Da Vinci and the Academy rather than the use of his somewhat limited military brain.

Mrs Tiggles
Stella Tiggles is the retired head of the Secret Intelligence service. She is a particular favourite of Da Vinci who treats her as his own mother. Mrs Tiggles' faithful companion is her cat, Bond... James Bond.

We were just like you once – ordinary schoolchildren leading ordinary lives. Then one day we all received a call from a strange character named Da Vinci. From that day on, we have led a double life – as secret members of Brain Academy!

Here are a few things you should know about the people you'll meet on your journey.

Maryland T. Wordsworth
M.T. Wordsworth is the president of the USA. Not the sharpest tool in the box, Maryland prefers to be known by his middle name, Texas, or 'Tex' for short. He takes great exception to being referred to as 'Mary' (which has happened in the past).

Buster Crimes
Buster is a really smooth dude and is in charge of the Police Force. His laid-back but efficient style has won him many friends, although these don't include Dr Hood or the agents of D.A.F.T. who regularly try to trick the coolest cop in town.

Sandy Buckett
The fearless Sandy Buckett is the head of the fire service. Sandy and her team of brave firefighters are always on hand, whether to extinguish the flames of chaos caused by the demented Dr Hood or just to rescue Mrs Tiggles' cat…

Echo the Eco-Warrior
Echo is the hippest chick around. Her love of nature and desire for justice will see her do anything to help an environmental cause – even if it means she's going to get her clothes dirty.

Victor Blastov
Victor Blastov is the leading scientist at the Space Agency. He once tried to build a rocket by himself but failed to get the lid off the glue. Victor often requires the services of the Academy, even if it's to set the video to record Dr Who.

Prince Barrington
Prince Barrington, or 'Bazza' as he is known to his friends, is the publicity-seeking heir to the throne. Always game for a laugh, the Prince will stop at nothing to raise money for worthy causes. A 'good egg' as his mother might say.

Working with Brain Academy

Do you get the idea? Now you've had the introduction we are going to show you the best way to use this book.

The plot

This tells you what the mission is about.

MISSION FILE 1:12

Line up!

Time: 6am sharp!
Place: Army Training Ground

General Cods-Wallop is training his best soldiers to form a perfectly straight line, ready for a parade in front of the Queen next week. Trouble is, he is trying to get them in perfect mathematical order at the same time. He knows there is a solution, he just can't crack it without the help of… Brain Academy!

If I can train them to polish my boots why can't they get in a straight line, Da Vinci?

Stand to attention, General, Huxley has a Training Mission that will knock them into shape!

The Training Mission

Huxley will give you some practice before sending you on the main mission.

TM

It's just a matter of taking things one step at a time. This straight line test will exercise your brain cells.

1) Place these numbers in the line so there is a difference of two between numbers next to each other.
2, 4, 4, 6, 6

2) Can you find another way to do this?

30

Each mission is divided up into different parts.

No one said this was easy. In fact that is why you have been chosen. Da Vinci will only take the best and he believes that includes you. Good luck!

Each book contains a number of 'missions' for you to take part in. You will work with the characters in Brain Academy to complete these missions.

The Main Mission
This is where you try to complete the challenge.

Now you can see how to form a straight line using a simple pattern, the General should be able to try to get his troops into some more tricky shapes.

1) Place the digits 1 – 8 in this number square so each side adds up to an odd total.

2) Can you find any other ways to do this?

3) Place the digits 1 – 6 in this triangle so that each side has an odd total.

4) Can you find any other ways to do this?

Good job! All this training means the parade will look fantastic for the Queen's visit. The soldiers have asked for some extra homework to learn their steps, so take the Da Vinci Challenge with them.

The Da Vinci Files

These problems are for the best Brain Academy recruits. Very tough. Are you tough enough?

Da Vinci files

Complete this number square so that each row, column and diagonal adds up to 15.
Only use the numbers 4, 5 and 6.

Huxley's Think Tank

Check all the rows.

Huxley's Think Tank
Huxley will download some useful tips onto your PDA to help you on each mission.

PS: See pages 44–47 for a useful process and hints and tips!

Square dance

Time: Before sunset
Place: Buster Crimes' police van

Buster Crimes is on a stakeout! The whole town is counting on him to bring music back into their homes as D.A.F.T. agents have broken into the radio station and stolen all the CDs. It's been quiet for days, but Buster has tracked the agents down to Green Street... now he needs the help of Brain Academy!

GREEN STREET

Da Vinci, I can't work out which houses the agents are in.

Don't be a square, Buster. This Training Mission will give you some clues!

Solve this Mission to identify the house numbers you need. Copy these and fill in the missing numbers from these pieces of a 100 square.

1)

23		
		35

2)

		79
96		

3)

5		

4)

| | | | 55 | |

M1

Brilliant! If you get this right you can creep into the back gardens and see which rooms the stolen CDs are being stored in.

Make four copies of this 16 square:

1	2	3	4
5	6	7	8
9	10	11	12
13	14	15	16

1) In the first grid, start at 0 and keep adding 2. Colour all your answers in the grid.

2) In the second grid, start at zero and keep adding 3. Colour all your answers in the grid.

3) In the third grid, do the same with 4s.

4) In the last grid, do the same with 5s.

You've got all the evidence you need, so take this Da Vinci Challenge and you can arrest the D.A.F.T. agents and get the radio station back on air!

Da Vinci files

Make five copies of a 25 square:
1) In the first grid, start at 0 and keep adding 2. Colour all your answers in the grid. In the second add 3s, the third 4s, the fourth 5s and the fifth 6s.
2) What do you notice about the patterns you find? You could try this with other number squares.

Huxley's Think Tank

Notice how the patterns change in different squares.

It's a tall story

Time: Homework o'clock
Place: At the zoo

For the first time ever, Echo is late handing in her Maths homework. She was supposed to measure the giraffes at the zoo each day, but they just keep growing and her sums can't keep up. Can you help Echo get her homework in before she gets a detention?

Help, Da Vinci! These animals are all growing faster than I can count!

Huxley will help you get a happy ending, Echo.

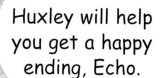

There's a pattern here if you just look at the way the numbers change as the animals grow day by day.

1) Fill in the missing numbers to make the number story for 3:

$$0 + \boxed{} = 3$$
$$1 + \boxed{} = 3$$
$$2 + \boxed{} = 3$$
$$3 + \boxed{} = 3$$

2) Write the number story for 4.

3) Write the number story for 5.

Have you worked it out yet? Try some more numbers and Echo will soon have all the answers she needs to get top marks!

1) Write the number story for 6.

2) Write the number story for 7.

3) Write the number stories for some more numbers.

Excellent! Complete the Da Vinci Challenge and Echo will get her homework on the teacher's desk in the morning.

Da Vinci files

Copy this table and fill in the missing numbers:

Number	3	4	5	6	7	8
Number of sums in the number story	4					

1) What pattern can you see?
2) Use your pattern to find which number story has twelve sums.
3) Check you answer to question 3 by writing the number story.
4) Test your pattern with other numbers.

Huxley's Think Tank

Write your number story in order so you don't miss any sums out. Start with a zero.

It's in the bag!

Time: 5.29pm
Place: The Pick'n'Mix Shop

Mrs Tiggles loves her favourite sweets so much, she wants to buy them for all of her friends. But she has spent so much time at the sweet shop, her cat James Bond thinks she has gone on holiday! Can you help her work out how to buy all the sweets she needs before James Bond needs feeding again? Quick... call Brain Academy!

James Bond will be getting hungry and I still can't decide how many sweets will fill this bag...

Huxley will get your shopping bag and James Bond's food bowl filled in no time!

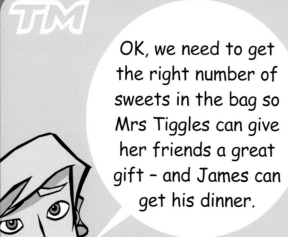

OK, we need to get the right number of sweets in the bag so Mrs Tiggles can give her friends a great gift – and James can get his dinner.

There are orange and green sweets in a bag.

1) Find all the ways you can have TWO sweets in the bag.

2) Find all the ways you can have THREE sweets in the bag.

3) Find all the ways you can have FOUR sweets in the bag.

4) Find all the ways you can have FIVE sweets in the bag.

Now Mrs Tiggles wanted to get herself some sweets too, with even more in the bag. How can she do this?

1) Use the answers to TM to fill in this table for orange and green sweets.

Number of sweets	2	3	4	5
Number of ways				

2) Describe the pattern in the table.

3) Use the pattern you found in 2) to work out how many ways for TEN coloured sweets in a bag.

Check your answer by writing out the different ways.

Great work, now Mrs Tiggles can get home before James Bond goes hungry and if you solve the Da Vinci Challenge the shopkeeper can serve some more customers!

Da Vinci files

Some boys and girls are waiting outside the shop.

If two children go into the shop the different pairs could be 2 boys, 1 boy and 1 girl or 2 girls. Find the different combinations of boys and girls if THREE children go into the shop.

Huxley's Think Tank

Work through the answers logically so you don't miss any answers. Use counters to help.

A Memory mystery

Time: Long past bedtime
Place: Hilary Kumar's study

Hilary Kumar can't get to sleep. She's locked some important papers in the Royal safe, but the Queen needs to sign them in the morning and Hilary can't remember what numbers she needs to open the combination lock and get the papers out. This sounds like a job for... Brain Academy.

Da Vinci, I've gone blank on these missing numbers.

Huxley will help you fill the gaps with his Training Mission.

TM

There are only THREE numbers that Hilary needs to know. She can remember TWO of them, can you help her find the last one?

1) Fill in the missing numbers for these calculations:

$4 + \boxed{} = 25$ $25 - 21 = \boxed{}$

$25 - \boxed{} = 4$ $\boxed{} - 4 = 21$

2) What do you notice about the calculations in Question 1?

3) Write down + and − calculations like those in 1) using the numbers 8, 14 and 22.

Now that Hilary has got the idea, can you help her to practise so she can get the papers out of the safe without any problems in the morning?

1) Write all the + and – calculations you can using the numbers 18, 32 and 50.

2) Write all the + and – calculations you can using the numbers 35, 65 and 100.

3) Make a set of + and – calculations for your own three numbers. Check they are right!

4) Fill in the missing numbers for these calculations:

$4 \times 2 = \boxed{}$ $\qquad$ $2 \times \boxed{} = 8$

$8 \div 4 = \boxed{}$ $\qquad$ $\boxed{} \div 2 = 4$

5) What do you notice about the calculations in Question 4?

Great work! Hilary won't forget how to find missing numbers again and if she gets the Da Vinci Challenge right, she can go back to bed and get a good night's sleep.

Da Vinci files

1) Find all the multiplication and division calculations you can using the numbers 3, 2 and 6.
2) Find all the multiplication and division calculations you can using the numbers 5, 4 and 20.
3) Investigate other calculations using $\times$ and $\div$.

Huxley's Think Tank

There should be two multiplication and two division calculations in a set. Make sure each set only uses three numbers.

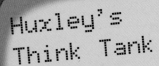

Mrs Tiggles's money-hunt!

Time: Just after lunch
Place: Mrs T's back garden

Mrs Tiggles was just about to pop out to buy herself a bar of chocolate, but she can't find her purse. She's hunted all through the house but she hasn't found it, so to get together some chocolate-buying money she decides to use her old metal detector to scan the garden for coins.

Any ideas how I can speed this hunt up, Da Vinci?

Huxley has a magnetic-tastic Mission for you, Stella!

1p 2p 5p 10p 20p 50p £1 £2

Mrs T needs to keep a track of the coins she is discovering with her detector. Let's help her!

Mrs Tiggles has two coins.

1) If the coins have exactly the same value, how much money might she have? Find as many answers as you can.

2) If one coin is worth double the other how much money might she have? Find as many answers as you can.

She has found lots of coins now but, oh dear, some of them have slipped down a crack in the patio.

1) Mrs Tiggles has lost one coin.
Work out which coin she has lost if:

a) She should have 40p but only has a 20p and a 10p.

b) She should have 70p but only has a 20p.

c) She should have 95p but only has a 20p, a 50p, and a 5p.

d) She should have £1.60 but only has a £1 and two 20ps.

2) Mrs Tiggles finds three coins that are worth 60p. Which three coins could they be? Find two answers.

Well done! Mrs T finally has enough to get her bar of chocolate, and if you get the Da Vinci challenge right, she'll have enough money to buy a can of lemonade too – all that metal detecting is thirsty work!

Da Vinci files

Mrs Tiggles finds ten silver coins. Altogether, they are worth £1.50. Which coins could they be? Find as many answers as you can.

Huxley's Think Tank

Use coins to help you work out these problems. Work in an order so you don't keep trying the same thing!

General Greenfingers

Time: Sunrise and shine
Place: Cods-Wallop's country garden

General Cods-Wallop has got up bright and early to plan out his new vegetable garden. But he only has an odd shaped piece of land to plant his potatoes in. Time for Brain Academy to lend a hand.

Da Vinci, my spuds are in a state with this funny shape, help!

Don't dump your seeds, General, Huxley will dig you out of trouble.

TM

Let's help the General understand what he can do in his garden by naming these odd shapes.

Name these shapes:
1a)    b)

c)

2) Using squared paper draw:
   a) two different hexagons
   b) two different pentagons
   c) two different octagons

Now the General understands what shape his land is, he needs to clear some space to plant his potatoes. He wants to plant them using TWO of these shapes. How can he do this using these shapes?

1) Put two of these shapes together to make:
a) a three sided shape
b) a four sided
c) a five sided shape
d) a six sided shape
e) a seven sided shape
f) an eight sided shape
g) a nine sided shape
h) a ten sided shape
You can use the same shape twice.

2) Find the names for as many of these shapes as you can.

Fantastic! The potato patch is dug and the carrots are ready to plant too. If you get the Da Vinci Challenge right, the General will also be able to plant some delicious runner beans to enjoy with his Sunday roast.

Da Vinci files

Can you put THREE of the original shapes from Mission 1 together to make shapes with 11, 12, 13, 14 and 15 sides?

Huxley's Think Tank

You can make more sides if the sides of the shapes hang over!

Save our seaside!

Time: Just before lunch
Place: Cesspool-by-Sea

The mayor of Cesspool-by-Sea has asked Echo to help clear up the mess on the beach. Tourists are tripping on the leftover litter and the smell is really stinky. The holidaymakers are all going home so she's going to need the help of Brain Academy to get them back.

Da Vinci, where must I start?

Do a survey to find out how much muck there is to clear. Remember to take a clothes peg for your nose!

1) If the symbol ● is for TWO pieces of rubbish, how could you show ONE piece?

2) If the symbol ● is for 4 pieces of rubbish:

    a) how many pieces of rubbish does ◗ show?

    b) how many pieces of rubbish does ◖ show?

    c) how many pieces of rubbish does ◕ show?

Rusty cans	Ice-cream wrappers	Crisp packets
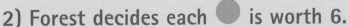		

So far, so good, but there is trouble ahead... Echo has lost the key for her graph. Can you help her work out the amounts of rubbish she and her friends have counted?

1) Echo decides each ⬤ is worth two.
   a) How many crisp packets are there?
   b) How many more rusty cans are there than ice-cream wrappers?
   c) How many pieces of rubbish are there altogether?

2) Forest decides each ⬤ is worth 6.
   a) How many rusty cans are there now?
   b) How many more crisp packets than ice-cream wrappers?
   c) How many pieces of rubbish are there altogether?

Brilliant! You've found the key to counting success. Now to clean up that beach, solve the Da Vinci Challenge and the tourists will start visiting Cesspool-by-Sea again.

Da Vinci files

1) Summer decides that Echo and Forest were wrong and that each ⬤ is worth 10. How many of each piece of rubbish does she need to pick up?

2) Make a pictogram of your own and ask a friend questions about it. Make sure you know the answers yoursellf!

Huxley's Think Tank

Use halving to find the values of a ◗ .

An odd day's work

Time: Friday afternoon
Place: Bank of Barrington

Prince Barrington is working out how many days his cooks have worked. If he doesn't get his sums right, the hardworking chefs won't get paid and if they go on strike, there will be a lot of hungry princes and princesses at his mansion. Help... he needs Brain Academy!

There's something 'odd' about these numbers, Da Vinci.

'Even' you can manage this, just get going on Huxley's Training Mission.

TM

Some of the cooks worked for an odd number of days and some worked for an even number of days.

1) Sort these numbers into groups of odd and even.

43, 82, 7, 99, 1, 21, 42, 64,

35, 50, 78, 24, 21, 78

2) Write down TEN more ODD numbers and TEN more EVEN numbers which are over 1000.

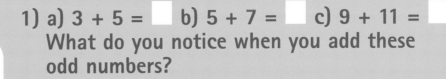

M1

Now the staff are sorted into groups, Bazza can start to organise their wages. He just needs to make sure he understands some odd and even facts first.

1) a) 3 + 5 = ☐ b) 5 + 7 = ☐ c) 9 + 11 = ☐
   What do you notice when you add these odd numbers?

2) Try adding other pairs of odd numbers. What do you notice?

3) a) 2 + 4 = ☐ b) 6 + 8 = ☐ c) 4 + 6 = ☐
   What do you notice when you add these even numbers?

4) Try adding other pairs of even numbers. What do you notice?

5) Now try adding an odd number to an even number. What happens?
   Try this with other odd and even numbers.

What a relief! Everyone has been paid and, to celebrate, the kitchen is busy making a toffee pudding fit for a king. Take the Da Vinci Challenge and this sticky problem won't happen ever again.

Da Vinci files

Remember the rules you learned above.

Without doing the sums, put these into two groups, one of sums with odd answers and one of sums with even answers.

345 + 27   68 + 121   652 + 666   75 + 63

123 + 442   56 + 27   90 + 24   35 + 126

Add some sums of your own to each group.

Huxley's Think Tank

Remember it is the last digit of each number you need to look at.

A whole ladder trouble!

Time: Early morning
Place: The Fire Station

Dr Hood and his D.A.F.T. agents have tampered with all the ladders on Sandy Buckett's fire-engines. A rung has been cut from each ladder and this could cause the brave firefighters to slip and fall. How will Sandy know which rungs have been removed? It's time to call Brain Academy!

I can't have my firefighters falling, Da Vinci!

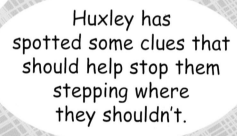

Huxley has spotted some clues that should help stop them stepping where they shouldn't.

TM

The D.A.F.T. agents have always removed the rungs that are halfway up the ladders, so you just need to work out these sums to see which step is missing.

For each of these pairs of numbers, find the number which is halfway between them.

1) Find the number halfway between 10 and 20.

2) Find the number halfway between 6 and 12.

3) Find the number halfway between 40 and 50.

Let's stop these villains' fun and work out which number rungs they might remove next. Then they can be stuck on with SuperStrong Glue and the D.A.F.T. agents' plot will be foiled!

1) Find the numbers halfway between these pairs:
a) 70 and 80
b) 90 and 110
c) 40 and 100

2) Now find the numbers halfway between each of these pairs:
a) 41 and 45
b) 18 and 28
c) 25 and 33

3) Find three pairs of numbers that six could be halfway between.

Genius! You've stopped the D.A.F.T. agents and made Sandy's ladders even safer. Take the Da Vinci Challenge to coat the rungs with honey, so if those snakes do come back, they'll get a sticky surprise!

Da Vinci files

Find the missing numbers:

1) 25 is halfway between _____ and 30.

2) 25 is halfway between 10 and _____.

3) 60 is halfway between 30 and _____.

4) Make up some of these problems and ask a friend to work them out.

Huxley's Think Tank

Use a number square to help you 'see' the answer!

It's a right-tangle

Time: Late on Saturday night
Place: Barrington Mansion

Prince Barrington is building a model of his mansion. He's got lots of different shaped blocks and an instruction book, but he can't work out how to make the corners. All of a sudden, he realises the answer to dealing with right angles is right in front of him!

Da Vinci, can I use this book to help me?

Just look at the pages, not at what they say!

If the Prince can understand what angles are all about, he'll be able to choose the right pieces to start shaping the walls of his model.

1) How many right angles are there on a plain piece of paper?

2) Draw different types of shapes that have right angles.

3) List five shapes that don't have right angles.

Complete this mission to help the Prince understand how to put the right pieces in the corners to make the rooms in his model.

1) List the shapes you can see which have right angles at their corners.

2) How many right angles can you find on the surface of a cube?

3) How many right angles can you find on the surface of a cuboid?

4) Try using different size cuboids. What do you notice about the number of right angles?

Prince Barrington will be building his house in no time. He'll even be able to put a roof on it if you get the Da Vinci Challenge right!

Da Vinci files

1) How many right angles can you find on the faces of an open cube (remember to count the ones on the inside and the outside)?

2) Count all the right angles on the faces of a box with an open lid.

Huxley's Think Tank

Use a corner torn off a piece of paper as a right angle measure. Make sure you only count each right angle once.

Double trouble

Time: Midday
Place: Dr Hood's lair

Hilary Kumar has gone undercover to spy on Dr Hood. She is pretending to be a waitress at a party the evil genius has planned. Dr Hood has invited his close friends, family and other villains that he plays golf with, but doesn't realise that Hilary is gaining useful information about what he does when he isn't plotting nasty crimes!

Psst! Da Vinci, can you help me untangle Hood's pesky party plot?

Sit tight behind that rosebush and wait for instructions from Huxley!

TM

Dr Hood and his D.A.F.T. agents like to confuse everyone – even people they like! You'll need to think in halves here...

To confuse people, Dr Hood only said half of each number he was thinking of.

1) He said he had 40 guests arriving at 3pm and they needed 25 parking places. How many guests was he expecting, at what time and how many parking places were needed?

2) He ordered 15 pizzas, 23 pies, 32 sausages and 50 drinks. How many of each did he really want?

The number you say	The number you mean
1	2
2	4

Hilary will pick up some more info on her tape recorder if she can understand Hood's code.

Agent A could not remember the code. He said double the number each time.

1) To sort out the mix up can you finish this table for the numbers up to 30 so Dr Hood can remember what he is supposed to say.

2) Agent A said they needed 4 get away cars.
   a) How many do they need?
   b) How many does Dr Hood think they need?

3) Dr Hood said they needed 10 disguises.
   a) How many disguises did Agent A bring?
   b) How many did they really need?

Well done for getting to the bottom of that D.A.F.T. talk. You'll be able to make a quick getaway without being discovered if you solve the Da Vinci Challenge!

Da Vinci files

1) Double 20. Double the answer. Double that answer. You now have a three digit number. How many times did you double it?
2) How many times do you have to double 50 to get a four digit number?
3) Find a number that you can double twice to get a three digit number.
4) Find a number that you can double four times to get a three digit number.

Huxley's Think Tank

Double the tens and then the units and add the answers together.

Line up!

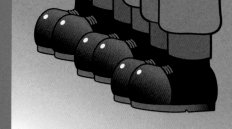

Time: 6am sharp!
Place: Army Training Ground

General Cods-Wallop is training his best soldiers to form a perfectly straight line, ready for a parade in front of the Queen next week. Trouble is, he is trying to get them in perfect mathematical order at the same time. He knows there is a solution, he just can't crack it without the help of... Brain Academy!

If I can train them to polish my boots why can't they get in a straight line, Da Vinci?

Stand to attention, General, Huxley has a Training Mission that will knock them into shape!

TM

It's just a matter of taking things one step at a time. This straight line test will exercise your brain cells.

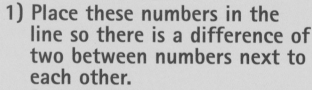

1) Place these numbers in the line so there is a difference of two between numbers next to each other.
2, 4, 4, 6, 6

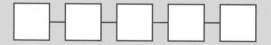

2) Can you find another way to do this?

1) Place the digits 1 – 8 in this number square so each side adds up to an odd total.

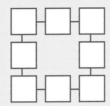

Now you can see how to form a straight line using a simple pattern, the General should be able to try to get his troops into some more tricky shapes.

2) Can you find any other ways to do this?

3) Place the digits 1 – 6 in this triangle so that each side has an odd total.

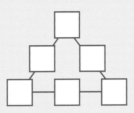

4) Can you find any other ways to do this?

Good job! All this training means the parade will look fantastic for the Queen's visit. The soldiers have asked for some extra homework to learn their steps, so take the Da Vinci Challenge with them.

Da Vinci files

Complete this number square so that each row, column and diagonal adds up to 15.
Only use the numbers 4, 5 and 6.

	5	
		4

Huxley's Think Tank

Check all the rows.

Flower power!

Time: Before dinner
Place: Sandy Buckett's house

Sandy Buckett has a secret admirer! She's been sent a lovely bunch of flowers and doesn't know who they are from. There are enough flowers to fill her whole house, and she is trying to get them into vases so they can all be seen. Can you and the Brain Academy help her arrange the blooms before they wilt away?

Da Vinci, I'm over-grown with fabulous flowers!

Sandy, help is on its way, just keep watering them during Huxley's Training Mission!

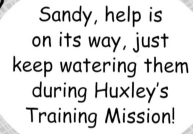

TM

Right, as there are so many flowers, you can arrange them in lots of different ways. Start with just two and move on.

There are red and yellow flowers.

1) Arrange TWO flowers as many ways as you can. (You can use both colours or just one). Try to find all FOUR ways.

2) There are EIGHT ways to arrange THREE flowers. How many of them can you find?

Some of the flowers are in vases and drinking up water, but there is only a long container left for the remaining plants.

The flowers still come in two colours, red and blue, but the colours at each end of the row must be the same.

1) Arrange TWO flowers as many ways as you can.

2) Arrange THREE flowers as many ways as you can.

3) a) How are the answers different to the answers in the TM?
   b) Why do you think they are different?

4) Arrange FOUR flowers as many ways as you can.

You saved all the flowers just in time. To find out who Sandy's secret admirer is, you need to solve the Da Vinci Challenge!

Da Vinci Files

1) Use the answers in M1 to complete this table for red and blue flowers when the end flowers have to match:

Number of flowers	2	3	4
Number of arrangements			

2) What pattern can you find?

3) Can you use your pattern to work out how many ways you could arrange FIVE flowers when there are two colours?

Huxley's Think Tank

Try to work in order so you don't miss any arrangements. Use R for red, Y for yellow.

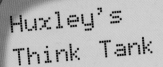

Shop 'til you drop

Time: Early Saturday morning
Place: Green Friends Shop

It's nearly Christmas and Echo has saved up her pocket money to buy her friends lovely presents from her favourite shop, Green Friends. She's secretly hoping that she'll have enough money left over from buying the gifts to sponsor some pets at the Animal Rescue Centre!

Is there any way I can save the animals and give great gifts, Da Vinci?

Let's see if we can make those pennies stretch, Echo!

TM

There's a sale on soft toys, so Echo might be lucky and get some bargains if she chooses wisely.

1) Echo buys THREE toy pandas costing 30p each.
   a) How much did she spend?
   b) How much change did she get from two 50p coins?

2) Echo buys a rainforest CD for £6.50 and some herbs for £2.50.
   a) How much did she spend?
   b) How much change did she get from £10?

M1

Echo has bought most of the gifts, but still needs some food for the pets she already has at home. Can you help her to save some more money?

Cat food 25p	Bird seed 50p	Milk 45p	Dog treats 20p	Fish food 40p

Echo buys TWO items.

1) What is the most she could spend?

2) If she spends 45p what did she buy?

3) If she spent 70p but didn't buy any bird seed, what did she buy?

4) What might she take home if she spent 65p? There are two answers. Can you find both of them?

Well done. Echo can now go to the rescue centre and sponsor some more animals. Get this Da Vinci Challenge right and she'll get a special certificate for her tree-house wall!

Da Vinci files

Echo sponsors FIVE abandoned kittens for £1 each, TWO puppies for £2 each and some rabbits. She gets £5 change from £20.

1) If she sponsors THREE rabbits how much did they cost each?

2) You have £20 to donate. If the rabbits cost £1.50, work out which animals you would sponsor and how much change you would get.

Huxley's Think Tank

Write down any amounts you work out.
Read the question after you have found the answer to check you have finished it.

Mrs T gets in a map flap!

Time: Far too late to be out
Place: The middle of nowhere

Mrs Tiggles thought it would be a nice treat to go with General Cods-Wallop on a night patrol with his new soldiers. The General let Mrs Tiggles read the map and now they are all completely lost! He sends out a special 'owl hoot' signal to call for help from the Brain Academy.

Coo-ee, Da Vinci, we're stuck in a wood and it's getting dark – help!

Keep Mrs T away from that map, we'll send emergency rescue!

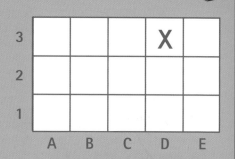

TIM

1) Cods-Wallop thinks they will find some food and a torch in a corner of the grid. The first corner square is A1. What are the others called?

2) Name all the squares in row 2.

3) Mrs Tiggles says the food must be where the X is. Name that square.

	A	B	C	D	E
3				X	
2					
1					

5
4
3
2
1

A B C D E F G H

N

The General decides he will read the map from now on. Follow the instructions to find a raft that will take them back down the river to Army HQ.

1) Start in B2. Go up 2, take 3 steps to the right, move into the square below, move left to the edge of the grid. Where did you finish?

2) Start in H5. Go West 6, South 3, East 4 and the answer is the square above that.

3) Describe a route to get from D4 to G1.

4) Describe a route to get from A1 to H4.

Well done. Now that Mrs T is just helping to row, you are on the way home. To get a nice hot bath for the tired troops when you get back, solve this map-reading Da Vinci Challenge.

Da Vinci files

1) Describe a route from B4 to H1 that uses 20 squares for the journey, including the first and last square.

2) Describe a route from A2 to F5 that:
   a) needs the least instructions
   b) goes in every column
   c) goes in every row.

Huxley's Think Tank

Name the column before the row (the bottom before the side!). It may help to draw the grid.

A fair share

Time: Late afternoon
Place: Barrington Mansion

Prince Barrington has decided that there is too much junk in his house, so he's having a car-boot sale and will donate all the money raised to his favourite sports charity P.O.N.G. (Princes Opposed to No Goals) to buy more footballs. There is so much to clear out, he can hardly carry it all to his fleet of cars!

Da Vinci, there is so much to carry, is there any way I can make this easier?

Huxley's Training Mission will make light work of this job!

TM

You need to divide all the small items into a few containers so there are less objects to carry down all the stairs at Bazza's mansion.

1) Share 14 china ducks between TWO boxes so that one box has 6 more ducks than the other.

2) Split 10 top hats between TWO boxes so that one box has an even number of hats more than the other. Find as many ways as you can to do this.

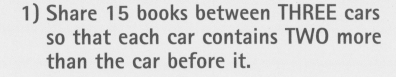

M1

1) Share 15 books between THREE cars so that each car contains TWO more than the car before it.

2) Split 26 paintings between FOUR cars so each car contains THREE more than the car before.

3) Split 18 lampshades between THREE cars so that each car contains a given number of lampshades more than the car before.
Find as many different ways as you can to do this.

Now most of the junk is in the garden, you need to get it into the different car boots.

There's so much to sell, the Prince is bound to raise lots of money for P.O.N.G.. To score even more money, complete the Da Vinci Challenge!

Da Vinci files

The Prince has sold his toys to some children. Starting with the youngest, each child gets 4 more toys than the child before (so the oldest gets the most toys!). The oldest gets 17 toys.

1) How many does the youngest child get?

2) How many toys did the Prince sell altogether?

3) How many children did the Prince sell his toys to?

Huxley's Think Tank

Give each one the extras first, then share out what you have left.

Fraction in-action

Time: Too early
Place: The White House

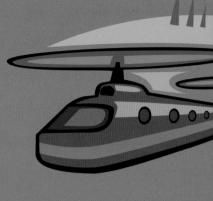

President Maryland T Wordsworth really needs some help today! He was woken up early by his helicopter landing and is so sleepy he can't get his work done properly. To keep him awake and fighting crime until bedtime he'll need your help. This sounds like a job for... Brain Academy!

I don't think I'll get anything right today, Da Vinci.

We'll all help to keep you awake and busy until bedtime, Tex!

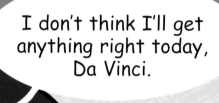

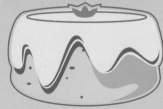

To cheer him up, one of Tex's Secret Agents has bought a cake for elevenses. But he's not sure how to cut it...

1) Tex cuts the cake into two and tells the agent that each piece is a half. Why might he be wrong?

2) a) How many ways can you cut a square cake into quarters (of the same shape) using only straight cuts?

b) How can you check that they are really quarters?

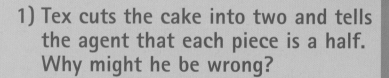

M1

Tex has asked his Secret Agents to help calculate how much time they spend working out in the White House gym.

1) Agent Andy spends $\frac{3}{10}$ of his time in the gym and another $\frac{2}{10}$ of his time washing out his gym kit.
   a) How much time does he spend on this altogether?
   b) Write it as a different fraction.

2) Agent Bill spends half of his time running around the White House lawn.
   a) How many quarters is this?
   b) If he spends another quarter of his time on this, how much will he have done?

Well done, Tex has stayed awake all day and his team have helped him complete all his jobs. To win him some earplugs to get a good night's sleep, take this Da Vinci Challenge!

Da Vinci files

A reward was offered for children to tell the President when they see a British D.A.F.T. agent trying to steal things from the shops in the USA.

Half of the reward money was given away and $\frac{1}{10}$ was spent.

1) How much was left?
2) This was shared between four children. What fraction did they get each?
3) Make a fraction sum for a friend to work out (but make you sure you know the answer!).

Huxley's Think Tank

You can only add fractions with the same denominator.

End games

Time: Victor tidied up!
Place: Victor's space station

The lab in Viktor Blastov's space station is in a real mess. He is trying to count what equipment he has left to build a mini computer, but there are so many pieces lying around he doesn't know where to start! If he doesn't get it tidy, he won't be allowed to use the lab for a week and he really wants to begin this new invention.

Da Vinci, vere do I begin?

Get yourself thinking in multiples to tackle this problem, Viktor!

To see what you have got left to build that computer, you need to count the different parts – and more than just one piece at a time!

1) Using a 100 square, start at 2 and count in 2s. Mark all the answers. What do you notice about the end of these numbers?
2) Now count in 5s and mark all the multiples of 5. What do you notice about the end of these numbers?
3) Now count in tens. What do you notice about the ends of these multiples of 10?

Now you've counted up the pieces, its time to get them back in the right places, then you'll be ready to start your new invention!

1) Complete these sentences with the right numbers:

a) Multiples of 2 end in ☐

b) Multiples of 5 end in ☐

c) Multiples of 10 end in ☐

2) Use your answers to predict what the last two digits are in these multiples.

a) Multiples of 20 end in ☐ and ☐.

b) Multiples of 50 end in ☐ and ☐.

c) Multiples of 100 end in ☐ and ☐.

d) Test your answers to see if you are right by writing the first 10 multiples of each number.

Cool! You've got all the pieces you need and you'll be allowed to use the lab again. By taking the Da Vinci Challenge, you'll get to stay up late to work on your new inventions for even longer.

Da Vinci files

132	400	60	123	550	700	95
248	150	30	140	170	125	371

1) Which of these numbers are multiples of 2?

2) Which of these numbers are multiples of 5?

3) Which of these numbers are multiples of 10?

4) Which of these numbers are multiples of 20?

5) Which of these numbers are multiples of 50?

Huxley's Think Tank

Some of the numbers will come on more than one list. Remember to look at the last digits in the number.

Mission Strategies 1

The TASC Problem Solving Wheel

TASC: Thinking Actively in a Social Context

Reflect
What have I learned?

Communicate
Who can I tell?

Evaluate
Did I succeed? Can I
think of another way?

Implement
Now let me do it!

Learn from experience

Communicate

What have
I learned?

Let's tell
someone.

Evaluate

How well
did I do?

Let's do it!

TA

Implement

We can learn to be expert thinkers!

Gather/organise

What do I know about this?

Identify

What is the task?

Generate

How many ideas can I think of?

Decide

Which is the best idea?

T A S C

Gather and Organise
What do I already know about this?

Identify
What am I trying to do?

Generate
How many ways can I do this?

Decide
Which is the best way?

Mission Strategies 2

MISSION FILE 1:1
Look across and down each square to help you with the Training Mission.
Look for patterns up and down and diagonally and see if you can carry them on!

MISSION FILE 1:2
Keep your work simple and remember, number stories are just sums! Da Vinci is
looking for a number that is one more than the number you start with.

MISSION FILE 1:3
Look for patterns in the numbers of ways you can have the sweets. Use the
letters G and O for the green and orange sweets and B and G for boys and girls.

MISSION FILE 1:4
Always remember that if you know one sum you know three more!
$1 + 2 = 3$ so $2 + 1 = 3$ and $3 - 1 = 2$ so $3 - 2 = 1$!

MISSION FILE 1:5
Think about what you are being asked to find out and what you know already
about coins. Use the Training Mission to help you answer the questions in
Mission 1 and the Da Vinci Files.

MISSION FILE 1:6
When you count the sides, put a pencil mark against each one you have counted
so you won't count them again. Your shapes might not look regular.

MISSION FILE 1:7
Decide which is the best way to do each of these questions. Carry out the work
carefully, checking as you go. Can you think of another way to make the key?

MISSION FILE 1:8
When you have noticed the rules about the numbers write them down so you will
remember to use them again.

MISSION FILE 1:9
Look at different ways of doing these problems. You could use a number line, try
writing the numbers out in order or circle the ones in the middle. Which idea
worked best?

MISSION FILE 1:10

A right angle is a corner. Look around you, how many corners or right angles can you see. Use the corner of a piece of paper to see whether a shape has a right angle.

MISSION FILE 1:11

Remember the doubles and halves you already know. They will help you answer lots of these questions.

MISSION FILE 1:12

Keeping the big numbers apart on all of these questions will be sure to help you. Decide the best way to answer the question before you write it down.

MISSION FILE 1:13

In the Da Vinci Files see if you can work out the pattern with two and three flowers and then use that information to 'estimate' the pattern with four flowers before trying another way.

MISSION FILE 1:14

Remember to identify what you are being asked to do first. Is the question asking for a number, amount of money or some words?

MISSION FILE 1:15

Always mark the column first and then the row. Go along the corridor and then up the stairs!

MISSION FILE 1:16

Can you think of a way to check your answer to these questions? Check the first one and then use your method to check the rest.

MISSION FILE 1:17

Look at your cake cuts to remember what you know about fractions. Using pictures will really help you to answer these questions.

MISSION FILE 1:18

'Predict' means using information you already know to make a sensible guess! So, use what you have learnt in the Training Mission to help you solve Mission 1.

nace

What is NACE?

NACE is a charity which was set up in 1984. It is an organisation that supports the teaching of 'more-able' pupils and helps all children find out what they are good at and to do their best.

What does NACE do?

NACE helps teachers by giving them advice, books, materials and training. Many teachers, headteachers, parents and governors join NACE. Members of NACE can use a special website which gives them useful advice, ideas and materials to help children to learn.

NACE helps thousands of schools and teachers every year. It also helps teachers and children in other countries, such as America and China.

How will this book help me?

Brain Academy Maths books challenge and help you to become better at learning and a better mathematician by:
• Thinking of and testing different solutions to problems
• Making connections to what you already know
• Making mistakes and learning from them
• Working with your teacher, by yourself and with others
• Expecting you to get better and to go on to the next book
• Learning skills which you can use in other subjects and out of school

We hope that you enjoy the books!

Write to **RISING STARS** and let us know how the books helped you to learn and what you would like to see in the next books.

RISING STARS
Rising Stars Ltd, 22 Grafton Street, London, W1S 4EX